Billy Sloan's

Rock and Pop Quiz Book

Other books available from the
Daily Record and Sunday Mail collection:

The 2002 Prize Crossword Book

The Jim Traynor/Hugh Keevins Sports Quiz Book

Joe Punter At The Races

The Tam Cowan Joke Book

You Are My Larsson, by Mark Guidi and Ewing Grahame

The Martin O'Neill, Story by Anna Smith David McCarthy

Videos available from the
Daily Record and Sunday Mail collection:

LUBO - A Gift From God

Billy Sloan's

Rock and Pop Quiz Book

First published 2001
by the Scottish Daily Record and Sunday Mail Ltd

ISBN 0-9513471-2-8

Copyright © Daily Record and Sunday Mail Ltd 2001

British Library Cataloguing in Publishing Data:
A catalogue record for this book is available
from the British Library.

Printed and bound in Great Britain

INTRODUCTION

I WENT to my first ever gig on October 21, 1971 – The Who at Green's Playhouse in Glasgow, seat number C32. How's that for a memory?

It sounds dramatic, but the experience changed my life. The lights, the volume, the sheer excitement – and my hero, guitarist Pete Townshend, on stage in the flesh.

Their amazing songs helped shape my life and set me off on a career path as a music journalist and broadcaster. So blame Pete.

From that moment on there were not enough hours in the day to listen to records or go to gigs. I still feel like that.

I'm not a snob about music. My tastes range from U2 to Frank Sinatra... Edith Piaf to The Sex Pistols... Travis to Michael Jackson.

I think I know a good band when I see one. Along the way, I'd like to think I've amassed some real music knowledge. Some folk say I'm a fan with a typewriter... it's the biggest compliment they can pay me.

I've compiled this book of pop quiz questions. If it gives you even a fraction of the pleasure the opening chords of Can't Explain by The Who gave me – you'll be doing okay.

So, eyes down and get answering. Good luck.

Billy Sloan.

Glasgow 2001.

GIRLS AND BOYS

THE charts have been dominated by a string of chart-topping boy bands, girl groups and male-female vocal acts.

How much do you know about the clean-cut pop idols whose posters adorn millions of walls?

1. NAME the boy band who had a UK hit single with a cover of the 1985 A-Ha song, Take On Me.

2. AND while we're on the subject of A-Ha ... who was their lead singer?

3. A SCOTS based vocal trio featuring Jimmy, Lee and Spike reformed in 2001. By what name are they better known?

4. IF you were singing along with H, Lee, Claire, Faye and Lisa, whose CD would you be playing?

5. WHO were the all-girl group formed by the sisters of Boyzone star Shane Lynch?

6. WHICH boy band played one of their earliest gigs in the Fifth Floor restaurant of the chic Harvey Nichols store in London?

7. NAME the act who made an embarrassing first television appearance on the Late Late Show with Gay Byrne in Dublin.

8. POP bad boy Brian Harvey fronted which successful male vocal act?

9. THIS US boy band were led by Donnie Wahlberg. Remember their name?

10. THINKING It Over was the debut hit of which group of flopstars turned popstars?

11. IN 1997, who sparked off a line-dancing craze with their debut UK hit, 5-6-7-8?

12. THIS US super girl trio scored a worldwide hit with the single and album, Survivor. Name them.

13. WHICH member of 5ive once dated singer Billie Piper?

14. FORMER All Saints' star Melanie Blatt joined forces with which dance act on the song, Twentyfourseven?

15. THIS US family trio had a massive hit with Mmmbop. What were they called?

16. WHO did Eternal star Esther Bennett marry in 1998?

17. AND which soccer star did her group mate Louise Nurding tie the knot with?

18. CAN you name the ex-member of Milan who became a star in EastEnders ... and also enjoyed a successful solo pop career?

19. BY what group name were Seventies boy-girl duo David Van Day and Therese Bazaar better known?

20. BEFORE Ricky Martin became a worldwide star he was a member of which Latin-style vocal act?

Answers on Page 12

Girls and Boys

1. A1
2. Morten Harket
3. 911
4. Steps
5. B*Witched
6. 5ive
7. Boyzone
8. East 17
9. New Kids On The Block
10. Liberty
11. Steps
12. Destiny's Child
13. Ritchie Neville
14. The Artful Dodger
15. Hanson
16. Shane Lynch of Boyzone
17. Liverpool star, Jamie Redknapp
18. Martine McCutcheon
19. Dollar
20. Menudo

THE NAME OF THE GAME

WHAT'S in a name? A heck of a lot if you're a pop star. For if you want to see your monicker go up in lights, better make it snappy and sexy.

Can you identify some of the acts behind these names?

1. BY what group name were Abs, J, Ritchie, Scott and Sean better known?

2. WHICH wildman of rock was born James Jewel Osterburg in Michigan in 1947?

3. THE late Beatles legend John Lennon shared a name with which British statesman.

4. TV hosts Ant 'n' Dec scored 13 Top 30 hit singles from 1994-1997 - but under which name?

5. MARK McLaughlin is one of Scotland's most famous pop stars ... who is he?

6. SOUL singer Smokey Robinson is a true Motown legend. What is his real Christian name?

7. DURAN Duran once had three unrelated members all called Taylor - what were their first names?

8. FRAN Healy is lead singer of Travis ... but can you name the group's drummer?

9. WHO were the original Jackson Five?

10. THIS US shock rocker is known to his mum as plain Brian Warner. Who is he?

Answers on Page 16

AND can you complete the names of these hit groups?

1. Grandmaster Flash and the ******* ****.

2. Wayne Fontana and the ***********.

3. Oxide & *********.

4. ***** Ant Farm.

5. **** ******* and the Bluecaps.

6. Bruce Springsteen and the * ***** ****.

7. *** and the Family Stone.

8. The Captain and ********.

9. ****** the Unstoppable Sex Machine.

10. Johnny Thunders and the *************.

Answers on Page 16

The Name of the Game

Section One:

1. 5ive; 2. Iggy Pop; 3. Winston after former Prime Minister, Winston Churchill; 4. PJ and Duncan; 5. Marti Pellow; 6. William; 7. John, Andy and Roger; 8. Neil Primrose; 9. Jackie, Tito, Jermaine, Marlon and Michael; 10. Marilyn Manson.

Section Two

1. Furious Five: 2. Mindbenders; 3. Neutrino; 4. Alien; 5. Gene Vincent; 6. E Street Band; 7. Sly; 8. Tennille; 9. Carter; 10. Heartbreakers.

IT'S ONLY WORDS

FROM the swinging Sixties ... to the naughty Nineties, our favourite rock stars provided the soundtrack for four decades – can you name the classic songs from these famous lyrics?

THE 1960s:

1.   The time to hesitate is through/No time to wallow in the mire.

2.   Cause her hair glows like the sun/And her eyes can light the sky.

3.   Loving you the way I do/I take you back/Without you I'd die dear.

4.   There's a five minute break/And that's all you take/For a cup of cold coffee/And a piece of cake.

5.   Hello Mrs Jones/How's your Bert's lumbago?

6.   I was only one day away from your arms.

7.   My girlfriend's run off with my car/And gone back to her ma and pa/Telling tales of drunkeness and cruelty.

8.   I was born with a plastic spoon in my mouth.

9.   You're the only girl my heart beats for/How I wish that you were mine.

10.   She's leaving now/Cause I just heard/The slamming of the door.

Answers on Page 22

THE 1970s:

1. Is it concrete all around/Or is it in my head.

2. There is no future/In England's dreaming.

3. I ain't no square with my corkscrew hair.

4. I wanna bite the hand that feeds me/I wanna bite that hand so badly.

5. Remember those basement parties/Your brother's karate.

6. The girls combed their hair in rear view mirrors/The boys tried to look so hard.

7. We could find plenty to do/And that would be all right.

8. Flying domestic flying/And when the stewardess is near/Do not show any fear.

9. Weary of the waltz/The mashed potato schmaltz.

10. You don't ever wanna see me again/Your brother's gonna kill me/And he's six foot ten.

Answers on Page 22

THE 1980s:

1. Listening to Marvin/All night long.

2. Well I look in the mirror/And it throws back the question.

3. Each tear that flows from my eyes/Brings back memories of you to me.

4. And when it was hot/She wouldn't wear much more.

5. Bands won't play no more/Too much fighting on the dance floor.

6. And she's sexually enlightened by Cosmopolitan.

7. Under the moonlight/the serious moonlight.

8. I've travelled the world and the seven seas/Everybody's looking for something.

9. We've got Marco, Merrick, Terry Lee/Gary Tibbs and yours truly.

10. Same as it ever was/Same as it ever was.

Answers on Page 24

THE 1990s:

1. I drink a whisky drink/I drink a lager drink.

2. Monopoly ... twenty one ... checkers ... and chess.

3. I'd like to do it/And you know you always had it coming.

4. So if you really love me/Come on and let it show.

5. I could buy you dinner in a fancy restaurant.

6. A man will beg/A man will crawl/On the sheer face of love/Like a fly on a wall.

7. There are many things that I would like to say to you/But I don't know how.

8. And through it all/She offers me protection.

9. All the people/So many people.

10. Slam it to the left/If you're having a good time.

Answers on Page 24

It's Only Words

The 1960s

1. Light My Fire - The Doors; 2. Pretty Flamingo - Manfred Mann; 3. Anyone Who Had A Heart - Cilla Black; 4. Matthew And Son - Cat Stevens; 5. Lazy Sunday Afternoon - The Small Faces; 6. Twenty Four Hours From Tulsa; 7. Sunny Afternoon - The Kinks; 8. Substitute - The Who; 9. My Cherie Amour - Stevie Wonder; 10. Ruby Don't Take Your Love To Town - Kenny Rogers.

The 1970s

1. All The Young Dudes - Mott The Hoople;
2. God Save The Queen - The Sex Pistols;
3. Telegram Sam - T-Rex; 4. Radio Radio - Elvis Costello; 5. You Wear It Well - Rod Stewart;
6. Born To Run - Bruce Springsteen; 7. Take Me Bak 'Ome - Slade; 8. This Town Ain't Big Enough For Both Of Us - Sparks; 9. Do The Strand - Roxy Music; 10. Can't Stand Losing You - The Police.

It's Only Words

ANSWERS:

The 1980s   1. True - Spandau Ballet; 2. Fergus Sings The Blues - Deacon Blue; 3. I Go To Sleep - The Pretenders; 4. Raspberry Beret - Prince; 5. Ghost Town - The Specials; 6. Perfect Skin - Lloyd Cole and the Commotions; 7. Let's Dance - David Bowie; 8. Sweet Dreams Are Made Of This - Eurythmics; 9. Ant Rap - Adam and the Ants; 10. Once In A Lifetime - Talking Heads.

The 1990s   1. Tubthumping - Chumbawamba; 2. Man On The Moon - R.E.M.; 3. Shoot You Down - The Stone Roses; 4. Love Is All Around - Wet Wet Wet; 5. Nothing Compares 2 U - Sinead O'Connor; 6. The Fly - U2; 7. Wonderwall - Oasis; 8. Angels - Robbie Williams; 9. Parklife - Blur; 10. Spice Up Your Life - The Spice Girls.

YOU'RE THE DEVIL IN DISGUISE

SOME pop stars don't think it's enough to have a stage name ... they want a nickname too.

Who are the performers nicknamed here?

1. WHICH pop chameleon was once known as the Thin White Duke?

2. WHO is the Godfather of Soul?

3. THIS US country star is called the Man in Black. Who is he?

4. NAME the superstar pair affectionately known as the Glimmer Twins.

5. WHICH US female superstar answers to the abbreviation ... J-Lo?

6. WHO is the self-crowned King of Pop?

7. THIS legendary vocalist was dubbed Ol' Blue Eyes. Who is he?

8. WHEN John Ritchie adopted a nickname he became a punk star. What was it?

9. HE was once filmed only from the waist up for dancing too provocatively. Who was the Pelvis?

10. WHICH Sixties soccer star was called ... the fifth Beatle?

Answers on Page 28

You're the Devil In Disguise

1. David Bowie;

2. James Brown;

3. Johnny Cash;

4. Mick Jagger and Keith Richards;

5. Jennifer Lopez;

6. Michael Jackson;

7. Frank Sinatra;

8. Sid Vicious;

9. Elvis Presley;

10. George Best.

SAY, SAY, SAY WHAT YOU WANT

Pop stars should always remember that famous motto ... Before opening mouth, make sure brain is in gear.

Which acts are responsible for these memorable quotes?

1. AT the Brits 2001, which superstar said - "If there's a better singer in England than Craig David ... then I'm Margaret Thatcher"?

2. WHICH world leader described the Manic Street Preachers' live show as being - "Louder than war"?

3. WHO famously described Robbie Williams as being - "That fat dancer from Take That"?

4. NAME the glamourous country music star who said: "It costs a lot to make me look so cheap".

5. THIS flamboyant gender-bender pop star raised eyebrows when he said: "Sex! I'd rather have a cup of tea". Name him.

6. WHO told a posh theatre audience: "Just rattle your jewellery"?

7. WHICH volatile star shouted - "Don't turn your back on me" - before thumping a TV chat show host?

8. THIS punk star told the crowd at his group's last ever gig - "Ever get the feeling you've been cheated?" Who was he?

9. IN 1974, who was Rolling Stone critic Jon Landau talking about when he said: "I have seen the future of rock 'n' roll"?

10. WHICH heavy metal wildman joked: "I've bitten the heads off bats, birds, dogs and cats ... and they all tasted wonderful"?

Answers on Page 32

SAY, SAY, SAY
WHAT YOU WANT

ANSWERS:

1.   Elton John;

2.   Cuban leader Fidel Castro;

3.   Noel Gallagher;

4.   Dolly Parton;

5.   Boy George;

6.   John Lennon;

7.   Grace Jones;

8.   Johnny Rotten;

9.   Bruce Springsteen;

10. Ozzy Osbourne.

IT TAKES TWO, BABY

Many classic songs have been performed by chart-topping duets ... some of them are unlikely partnerships

Name the famous names behind these hits.

1. FRANK Sinatra duetted with this Irish rocker on a new version of I've Got You Under My Skin. Who was he?

2. ELTON John scored his first UK No. 1 hit single in 1976 with Don't Go Breaking My Heart. Name his female partner.

3. WHO recorded Dancing In The Street together for charity in 1985?

4. SPICE Girl Mel C recruited this Canadian rock star to help her out on When You're Gone. Name him.

5. WHICH two US rockers had a vocal sparring match on the 1981 hit, Dead Ringer For Love?

6. SOFT Cell star Marc Almond hit No. 1 in 1989 with Something's Gotten Hold Of My Heart. Can you recall the Sixties' star who duetted with him?

7. ANNIE Lennox fulfilled a lifelong ambition when she recorded Sisters Are Doin' It For Themselves with which soul legend?

8. IN 2000, boy band 5ive opened the Brit Awards show performing We Will Rock You with which rock superstars?

9. WHICH rock guitar legend performed with US rap star Puff Daddy on the hit single Come With Me?

10. IN 1985, reggae band UB40 scored their second UK No. 1 with I Got You Babe. Name group singer Ali Campbell's female co-star on the track.

Answers on Page 36

11. DAVID Bowie had a 1982 Christmas hit when he performed a duet with legendary crooner, Bing Crosby. What was the title of the single?

12. WHO performed a hit duet in 1996 with the single If You Ever?

13. WHICH Scots female singer guested with Prince on the 1987 smash hit, U Got The Look?

14. PETER Gabriel and Kate Bush got together in 1986 on which Top 10 song?

15. WHO urged us to "jump on board and take a ride" in the smash hit single, Kids?

16. WHICH Welsh supergroup joined Tom Jones on a cover version of the old Three Dog Night hit, Mamma Told Me Not To Come?

17. AND Eminem's rap classic Stan featured a vocal sample from which UK female artist?

18. WHICH two Motown giants duetted on Endless Love?

19. ROBERT Palmer worked with some old mates on his 1990 hit, I'll Be Your Baby Tonight. Who were they?

20. WHICH pair of music legends had a hit in 1989 with the gospel song, Whenever God Shines His Light?

Answers on Page 36

IT TAKES TWO, BABY

ANSWERS:

1. Bono of U2; 2. Kiki Dee; 3. David Bowie and Mick Jagger; 4. Bryan Adams; 5. Meat Loaf and Cher; 6. Gene Pitney; 7. Aretha Franklin; 8. Brian May and Roger Taylor of Queen; 9. Jimmy Page of Led Zeppelin; 10. Chrissie Hynde; 11. Peace On Earth - Little Drummer Boy; 12. East 17 & Gabrielle; 13. Sheena Easton; 14. Don't Give Up; 15. Robbie Williams & Kylie Minogue; 16. Stereophonics; 17. Dido; 18. Diana Ross & Lionel Richie; 19. UB40; 20. Cliff Richard & Van Morrison.

YOU GOTTA ROLL WITH IT

A DECADE ago, Oasis exploded on to the music scene and became the biggest UK band of the 1990s.

What do you remember about the controversial career of pop bad boys, Liam and Noel Gallagher.

1. THE group made their live debut on August 18, 1991. What was the venue?

2. THEY were spotted by Alan McGhee two years later at King Tut's in Glasgow. Who had the Scots pop svengali actually gone along to see?

3. OASIS performed a Beatles' classic as part of their brief four-song set at King Tut's. What was it?

4. NAME the original Oasis drummer?

5. WHO fills the drum stool in the line-up now?

6. WHAT was the title of Oasis's first hit single?

7. AND what song gave them their first UK No.1?

8. THE group once headlined a gig in a circus tent at which Scottish seaside venue?

9. ROD Stewart covered a track from their debut album Definitely Maybe. What was it?

10. WHAT was original Oasis' rhythm guitarist Bonehead's real name?

Answers on Page 40

11. IN 1995, Oasis and Blur went head to head in the UK singles charts. What was the Oasis track called?

12. BUT Blur pipped them to the No. 1 spot with which single?

13. What's ex-bass player Guigsy's proper name?

14. WHICH Oasis classic includes the immortal line: "I live my life by the stars that shine/People say it's just a waste of time"?

15. THE group set the UK attendance record when they played two gigs to a total of 250,000 fans in 1996. Where?

16. WHO replaced Bonehead and Guigsy in the band line-up?

17. LAST year, Oasis did a co-headline tour of North and South America with which US wildmen?

18. WHAT was the title of Oasis' live album recorded on stage at Wembley Stadium?

19. WHICH artist did Noel Gallagher make a guest appearance with at T In The Park 2001?

20. IN 1996, Liam and Noel fulfiled a lifelong ambition by headlining at the home of their favourite football team. Name the team ... and the venue.

Answers on Page 40

YOU GOTTA ROLL WITH IT

1. Manchester Boardwalk; 2. 18 Wheeler; 3. I Am
The Walrus; 4. Tony McCarroll; 5. Alan White;
6. Supersonic; 7. Some Might Say; 8. Irvine Beach;
9. Cigarettes And Alcohol; 10. Paul Arthurs;
11. Roll With It; 12. Country House; 13. Paul
McGuigan; 14. Rock 'n' Roll Star; 15. Knebworth;
16. Gem Archer and Andy Bell; 17. The Black
Crowes; 18. Familiar To Millions; 19. Paul Weller;
20. Manchester City - Maine Road.

ONE SINGER ...
ONE SONG

FROM Elvis Presley to George Michael the pop world has had more than its share of great singers.

Can you name the star vocalists who fronted these famous groups?

1. Free.

2. Guns 'n' Roses.

3. Jamiroquai.

4. Garbage.

5. Led Zeppelin.

6. The Who.

7. Stereophonics.

8. The Stone Roses.

9. Coldplay.

10. Deep Purple.

Answers on Page 44

AND for which top acts did these singers strut their stuff?

1. James Dean Bradfield.

2. Julian Casablancas.

3. Terry Hall.

4. Martin Fry.

5. Roddy Frame.

6. Peter Gabriel.

7. Cerys Matthews.

8. Ian Curtis.

9. Brett Anderson.

10. Brian Connolly.

Answers on Page 44

ONE SINGER, ONE SONG

ANSWERS:

Section One

    1. Paul Rodgers; 2. Axl Rose; 3. Jay Kay;
4. Shirley Manson; 5. Robert Plant; 6. Roger
Daltrey; 7. Kelly Jones; 8. Ian Brown; 9. Chris
Martin; 10. Ian Gillan.

Section Two

    1. The Manic Street Preachers; 2. The Strokes;
3. The Specials and Fun Boy Three; 4. ABC;
5. Aztec Camera; 6. Genesis; 7. Catatonia; 8. Joy
Division; 9. Suede. 10. The Sweet.

ONE SINGER
ONE SONG

HOME IS WHERE THE HEART IS

SCOTS musicians have written their own chapter in the pop history books.

How much do you know about the local acts who have stormed the charts all around the world?

1. WHICH group were formed by four mates at Clydebank High School?

2. NAME the 1979 debut album by Simple Minds.

3. LLOYD Cole and the Commotions were one of our most successful pop acts. Is group frontman Lloyd a Scot?

4. WHAT was the chart-topping act formed by brothers Ken and David McCluskey?

5. WHO was spotted working as a waitress in The Spaghetti Factory in Glasgow - and offered a role in the movie Gregory's Girl by top director Bill Forsyth?

6. IF you saw the songwriting credit (Currie/Harvie) on a CD ... which group would you be listening to?

7. WHICH top Scots singer married his group's backing vocalist?

8. NAME the influential indie label founded in a tenement at 185 West Princess Street, Glasgow, in 1980.

9. WHO were the first act to record for the label ... and what was the title of their single?

10. WHAT is the Scots connection in rock supergroup AC/DC?

Answers on Page 48

11. WHICH controversial act once featured Bobby Gillespie of Primal Scream on drums?

12. AND which ex-member of The Stone Roses joined the Primals on bass?

13. THIS Scots duo released a cheeky cover of David Bowie's Boys Keep Swinging as their first single. Who were they?

14. A WALK Across The Rooftops, Hats and Peace At Last are albums by which trio?

15. NAME the Stealer's Wheel song used in the sound track of the film, Reservoir Dogs.

16. BEFORE Travis hit the big time ... what were they called?

17. THIS mysterious Glasgow group made their debut with the album Tigermilk. Who are they?

18. WHICH legendary Scots singer had hits with Darlin' and Caledonia?

19. WHO were the Fife punk band formed by singer Richard Jobson?

20. AND which Edinburgh punk outfit had a female star with the bizarre name ... Faye Fife?

Answers on Page 48

HOME IS WHERE THE HEART IS

1. Wet Wet Wet; 2. Life In A Day; 3. No, he's English - born in Derbyshire; 4. The Bluebells; 5. Clare Grogan of Altered Images; 6. Del Amitri; 7. Deacon Blue's Ricky Ross who wed group member Lorraine McIntosh; 8. Postcard Records; 9. Orange Juice – Falling And Laughing; 10. Glasgow born brothers, Angus and Malcolm Young; 11. The Jesus And Mary Chain; 12. Mani; 13. The Associates; 14. The Blue Nile; 15. Stuck In The Middle With You; 16. Glass Onion; 17. Belle and Sebastian; 18. Frankie Miller; 19. The Skids; 20. The Rezillos.

YOU CAME TO THE RIGHT PLACE

OVER the years, tens of thousands of Scots rock fans have flocked to the SECC, the Barrowland and King Tut's in Glasgow

What do you really know about our three top venues?

THE SECC:

1. WHO were the first ever act to headline a gig at the SECC in 1985?

2. CAN you remember the then up-and-coming act who supported them?

3. WHAT is the nickname given to this multi-capacity venue?

4. WHICH US superstar gave his chauffeur the night off ... and arrived at the SECC's stage door on a mountain bike?

5. WHICH super duo played a sell out gig in Hall 4 in November 1999 as part of their reunion tour?

6. WHO appeared at the SECC with his spectacular Lord of the Dance show?

7. NAME the blues legend who received an award for headlining the first gig at the Clyde Auditorium.

8. IN 1990, this superstar was driven by golf buggy from Hall 4 to Hall 1 to wave to fans watching his show on CCTV. Who was he?

9. WHO holds the record for playing the most sell-out SECC gigs in one year?

10. WHICH US superstar recorded a live version of Lucky Town at the SECC for a screening on Top Of The Pops?

Answers on Page 52

11. NAME the act whose pet dog appeared on stage with them when they sold out Hall 4 in 2000.

12. THIS solo star warmed up for his gig at the venue in 1999 by challenging the local stage crew to a game of football in the empty hall. Who was he?

13. WHICH former punk rocker supported The Who at the venue in 2000?

14. WHO was the superstar who got "chopped to pieces" when he walked into an industrial fan at the rear of the stage?

15. WHAT was different about the staging of Neil Diamond's two sell-out gigs at the SECC?

16. WHO made one of his earliest appearances at the venue nursing a broken ankle?

17. IN which year did ex-Beatle Paul McCartney perform there during his Flowers In The Dirt world tour?

18. WHO duetted with Tom Jones at the Clyde Auditorium in November 2000?

19. WHICH megastar played two shows at the SECC without ever setting foot in the venue?

20. NAME the singer who used a steam wallpaper stripper to help clear his tubes when he was on stage.

Answers on Page 52

YOU CAME TO THE RIGHT PLACE

ANSWERS:

The SECC:

1. UB40; 2. Simply Red; 3. The Big Red Shed;
4. Bob Dylan; 5. Eurythmics; 6. Michael Flatley;
7. B.B. King; 8. Pavarotti; 9. Wet Wet Wet in 1995
and Boyzone in 1999 ... with 10 shows each;
10. Bruce Springsteen; 11. The Tweenies, whose dog
Doodles is part of their act; 12. Robbie Williams;
13. Ex-Clash singer Joe Strummer; 14. David
Copperfield; 15. Neil performed in-the-round on a
revolving stage; 16. Shane Lynch of Boyzone;
17. 1990; 18. Kelly Jones of Stereophonics on Mama
Told Me Not To Come; 19. Elvis Presley who
"performed" two virtual gigs; 20. Sting.

BARROWLAND:

1. IN 1983, which Scots supergroup helped relaunch Barrowland as a live venue when they shot a video there?

2. WHAT was the title of the song?

3. AND which superstar joined Simple Minds singer Jim Kerr on stage at the venue the following year to duet on New Gold Dream?

4. NAME the US supergroup who sold out Barrowland on their 1988 Green tour.

5. WHICH two bands played there on the same day in 1984 for BBC 2's live Rock Around The Clock show?

6. THIS US rap group performed a controversial stage act at the Barras which featured naked girls dancing in steel cages. Who were they?

7. WHO were the top band who played an emotional farewell gig at Barrowland on May 31, 2000?

8. NAME the pop bad boy who nearly sparked a riot when he claimed he'd "lost his voice" after singing just three songs ... and went back to his hotel.

Answers on Page 56

9. WHICH veggie star threatened to scrap her show because she could smell burgers being sold in the venue?

10. WHO holds the record for the biggest run of sell-out gigs at Barrowland?

11. WHICH band played four consecutive sell-out shows from December 1-4, 1992?

12. WHICH Scots band supported King when they played a Hogmanay show in 1986 for BBC 2's Whistle Test?

13. WHO was the sexy US star who named Barrowland as her favourite gig during an MTV profile?

14. WHICH female artist recorded a song about dancing at the Barrowland?

15. NAME the former US Golden Gloves boxing champion who sold out two gigs at the venue?

Answers on Page 56

YOU CAME TO THE RIGHT PLACE

ANSWERS:

Barrowland:

1. Simple Minds: 2. Waterfront; 3. Bono of U2;
4. R.E.M.; 5. Aztec Camera and The Cure; 6. The
Beastie Boys; 7. Big Country; 8. Liam Gallagher of
Oasis; 9. Chrissie Hynde of The Pretenders;
10. Ocean Colour Scene with five gigs; 11. Faith
No More; 12. Wet Wet Wet; 13. Debbie Harry of
Blondie; 14. Eddi Reader; 15. Terence Trent D'Arby.

KING TUT'S:

YOU CAME TO THE RIGHT PLACE

1. WHICH group wore a disguise of hippie wigs and psychedelic clothes to play a secret gig as Nug?

2. WHAT happened just three hours before Crowded House made their debut Tut's appearance in 1991

3. NAME the band who took the Tut's stage as On Standby ... a tribute act to themselves.

4. THIS supergroup appeared at the venue a few weeks after their single Creep flopped. Who were they?

5. WHO offered a reward for the return of his full size dog costume after it vanished from his dressing room?

6. WHICH tribute band pelted the audience with chocolate money when they made their debut at the club?

7. BEFORE Tut's opened it's doors in February 1990, it was a venue for local acts. What was it called then?

8. ON January 2001, the sons of which famous US songwriter appeared at Tut's. Who were they?

9. IN March 1991, Manic Street Preachers played the venue as a four piece. Who was the other member in the line-up?

10. WHO played a surprise show last April to launch the album, Deep Down And Dirty?

Answers on Page 58

YOU CAME TO THE RIGHT PLACE

ANSWERS:

King Tut's:

1. Gun; 2. Tim Finn was ejected from the group;
3. Shed Seven; 4. Radiohead; 5. Julian Cope; 6.
Bjorn Again; 7. Saints and Sinners; 8. The Webb
Brothers – sons of Jimmy Webb; 9. Guitarist Richie
Edwards, who later went missing; 10. Stereo MCs.

WE'VE GOT YOU COVERED

THERE is no doubt that the sound quality of a CD is superb ... but the packaging is inferior to old-style 12-inch Lps

How many classic albums can you name from the descriptions of these famous sleeves?

1. ON which 1974 album featured David Bowie as a futuristic half-man, half-dog?

2. WHICH now famous TV chef helped bake the cake which appeared on The Rolling Stones' LP, Let It Bleed?

3. AND which famous artist designed the Stones' ground-breaking Sticky Fingers cover?

4. NAME the Hollywood sex symbol who initially refused to let her image appear on the sleeve of The Beatles' classic Sergeant Pepper's album ... because she didn't want to a member of a "lonely hearts club band".

5. WHAT is the swimming baby on the sleeve of Nirvana's album Nevermind trying to grab?

6. IN 1968, The Small Faces released an album in a ground-breaking circular sleeve. What was it called?

7. WHICH Roxy Music sleeve featured lead singer Bryan's Ferry's then girlfriend Jerry Hall on the cover?

8. IN which European airport did U2 do the cover shoot for their latest album, All That You Can't Leave Behind?

9. NAME the punk act who released a their album Metal Box in a round tin.

10. WHICH movie soundtrack album featured John Travolta and Olivia Newton-John snuggling up on the sleeve?

Answers on Page 62

11. ON which classic Who album did the group appear to be taking a leak against a concrete pillar?

12. NAME the mega-selling Fleetwood Mac album which featured drummer Mick Fleetwood on the sleeve wearing tights.

13. THE Beatles were photographed on a zebra crossing for which album cover?

14. WHAT was the location for the cover of the Travis album, The Invisible Band?

15. WHICH Oasis album sleeve featured an aerial photograph of New York skyscrapers?

16. NAME the Andy Warhol designed sleeve which features a plain white cover with a banana on it.

17. WHICH album cover has a photograph of a nude John Lennon and Yoko Ono?

18. THE sleeve of this famous LP stars celebrities such as Michael Parkinson, Kenny Lynch and Clement Freud. Name it.

19. WHICH Seventies rock band had a live album packaged in a mock envelope ... with their portraits as "postage stamps"?

20. NAME the all-time classic LP which features a motorcyle exploding out of the ground in a graveyard.

Answers on Page 62

WE'VE GOT YOU COVERED

ANSWERS:

1. Diamond Dogs; 2. Delia Smith; 3. Andy
Warhol; 4. Mae West; 5. A Banknote; 6. Ogden's
Nut Gone Flake; 7. Siren; 8. Charles de Gaulle in
Paris; 9. Public Image Limited; 10. Grease;
11. Who's Next; 12. Rumours; 13. Abbey Road;
14. A Forest; 15. Standing On The Shoulder Of
Giants. 16. The Velvet Underground & Nico;
17. Two Virgins; 18. Band On The Run by Wings;
19. Free; 20. Bat Out Of Hell by Meat Loaf.

YOU GOT SOUL

WHEN it comes to soul music, you can't beat the magic of Motown.

BUT how good is your knowledge of the legendary US record label which was launched in 1959?

1. WHO founded the Motown record label?

2. IN which US city was the label based?

3. WHAT was the label originally called?

4. CAN you remember the name given to the Motown studio?

5. THE song Shop Around gave Motown it's first major US chart hit in 1961. Who recorded it?

6. THE girl who worked in the company's tape store was asked to make a record. What was her name?

7. AND who were her backing group?

8. COMPLETE the name of the famous Motown songwriting team – Holland, ****** and ******.

9. WHICH Motown vocal act invented their own dance steps called ... The Shuffle?

10. WHAT name did Motown give three aspiring singers Diana Ross, Mary Wells and Florence Ballard?

Answers on Page 66

11. NAME their first UK hit from 1964.

12. WHO discovered The Jackson Five and recommended that Motown sign them?

13. WHO was the blind, harmonica playing teenager who became a Motown legend?

14. COMPLETE the label's famous slogan: The Sound of ***** *******.

15. WHO married the Motown founder's sister Anna and became one of the the label's most famous singing stars?

16. WHICH famous Motown act penned the label's smash hits The Way You Do The Things You Do and Get Ready?

17. NAME the chart-topping Motown band formed by a then-unknown Lionel Richie.

18. WHICH female star hit No.1 in the US in 1964 with the classic My Guy?

19. FULFILLINGNESS' First Finale and Songs In The Key Of Life were landmark albums for which Motown act?

20. LEVI Stubbs was lead singer of which Motown vocal act?

Answers on Page 66

YOU GOT SOUL

1. Berry Gordy; 2. Detroit; 3. Tamla Records;
4. Hitsville USA; 5. The Miracles; 6. Martha Reeves;
7. The Vandellas; 8. Dozier, Holland; 9. The
Temptations; 10. The Supremes; 11. Where Did
Our Love Go; 12. Diana Ross; 13. Little Stevie
Wonder; 14. Young America; 15. Marvin Gaye;
16. Smokey Robinson; 17. The Commodores;
18. Mary Wells; 19. Stevie Wonder; 20. The Four
Tops.

AND can you identify these classic Motown hits from the following lyrics?

1. "I'm just a fella/I've got a one ... one track mind".

2. "All the time I think of you/You're with me no matter what you do".

3. "Let the music play on ... play on ... play on".

4. "And I just wanna live/I just wanna give/I'm completely positive".

5. "Didn't I treat you right now baby/Didn't I".

6. "If you're gonna play hide and seek with love/Let me remind you/It's all right".

7. "One can worship on a star/Two can make that dream come true".

8. "Like birds of a feather we stick together".

9. "So if you feel like loving me/And if you've got the notion".

10. "She said love don't come easy/It's a game of give and take".

Answers on Page 70

11. "All you need is music/Sweet music/There'll be music everywhere".

12. "I can't survive/Can't stay alive/Without your love".

13. "If he always keeps you dreaming/You won't have a lonely hour".

14. "She's a very kooky girl/The kind you don't take home to mother".

15. "Hey world we've got a great big job to do/Yeah we need you".

16. "It keeps on haunting me/Just keeps on reminding me".

17. "You can love me if you wanna/But I do declare/When I get restless/I gotta move somewhere".

18. "It was the third of December/That day I'll always remember".

19. "What is it good for/Absolutely nothing".

20. "Sugar pie honey bunch/You know that I love you".

Answers on Page 70

YOU GOT SOUL

1. Too Busy Thinking About My Baby – The Four Tops; 2. Let's Get Serious – Jermaine Jackson; 3. All Night Long – Lionel Richie; 4. I'm Coming Out – Diana Ross; 5. Standing In The Shadows Of Love – The Four Tops; 6. Get Ready – The Temptations; 7. It Takes Two – Marvin Gaye & Kim Weston; 8. My Guy – Mary Wells; 9. I Second That Emotion – Smokey Robinson and the Miracles; 10. You Can't Hurry Love – The Supremes; 11. Dancing In The Street – Martha and the Vandellas; 12. Don't Leave Me This Way – Thelma Houston; 13. The Night – Franki Valli and the Four Seasons; 14. Superfreak – Rick James; 15. The Onion Song – Marvin Gaye & Tammi Terrell; 16. There's A Ghost In My House – R. Dean Taylor; 17. (I'm A) Roadrunner – Jr. Walker and the Allstars; 18. Papa Was A Rolling Stone – The Temptations; 19. War – Edwin Starr; 20. I Can't Help Myself – The Four Tops.

YOU GOT SOUL

VIDEO KILLED THE RADIO STAR ...

THIS year, music channel MTV celebrated its 29th anniversary with a non-stop menu of all-star videos. We all have our favourite pop promo ... whether it's the Michael Jackson's lavish Thriller or the more simple Nothing Compares 2 U by Sinead O'Connor.

So here's a test of your knowledge of the pop video revolution.

1. THE video for which hit song features singer Chris Martin walking along a deserted, rainswept beach?

2. R.E.M. and Kate Pearson of the B52s joined forces on what promo?

3. WHO directed the video for Michael Jackson's epic, Thriller?

4. POLITICAL cartoonist Gerald Scarfe produced a series of disturbing images for which Pink Floyd hit?

5. IN which promo did Paul McCartney dress up as Hank Marvin of The Shadows and Ron Mael of Sparks?

6. FOR the video of this 1974 hit The Rolling Stones were covered in foam. What was it called?

7. MADONNA dressed as a cowgirl and did a sexy line-dance in which video?

8. ROBERT Palmer had a backing band of beautiful models – all dressed identically – in which promo?

9. AND talking of sexy models, can you remember the George Michael video that starred Linda Evangelista and Tyra Banks?

10. DURAN Duran were filmed riding the crest of a wave on a yacht for which promo?

Answers on Page 76

11. NELLY Furtado got covered in mud when she rolled around in a swamp. Name the video.

12. IN which 2001 promo were Scots band Travis "abducted" by aliens?

13. AND in the same year, which video featured ex-Stone Roses singer Ian Brown cycling backwards through Soho in London?

14. US superstar Jennifer Lopez dressed in leather and sped down the highway on a motorbike in which video?

15. IN the video for which Radiohead song did Thom Yorke lie on the roof of a mobile home in a trailer park?

16. EMMA Bunton wore a skimpy see-through negligee as she danced along a rocky beach for which video?

17. NAME the 1987 hit in which U2 shot the video on a rooftop in San Francisco.

18. IN which 2001 video did a toy robot recreate the famous dance routines of John Travolta in Saturday Night Fever and Michael Jackson's famous moon walk?

19. LIAM Gallagher had to sit perched on a chair 30ft. up a wall. What was the song?

20. NAME the Basement Jaxx promo in which the group became monkeys.

Answers on Page 76

21. NAME the US rock supergroup and the US rap band who appeared in the video for Walk This Way.

22. IN which award-winning promo did Jamiroquai star Jay Kay dance in a room with moving furniture?

23. THIS weird video by The Avalanches featured a dancing chimp, a 10ft tall parrot and a band comprised of OAPs. What was the song?

24. WHICH Seventies star appeared with actor Ricky Tomlinson in the promo for the single, Are U Looking At Me?

25. WHO played travelling salesmen selling a miracle cure in the video for the 1983 hit, Say Say Say.

26. IN which classic David Bowie video did Steve Strange of Visage have a cameo role?

27. PAUL Simon was continually upstaged by which Hollywood actor in the promo for You Can Call Me Al?

28. WHO choreographed Talking Heads' Once In A Lifetime video ... and also had a UK hit in 1982 with Mickey?

29. WHICH Spandau Ballet video was shot at the trendy Beat Route night club?

30. IN which Steps' video set in a hospital did Lisa, Faye and Claire dress up as sexy nurses?

Answers on Page 76

VIDEO KILLED THE RADIO STAR ...

ANSWERS:

1. Yellow by Coldplay; 2. Shiny Happy People;
3. John Landis; 4. Another Brick In The Wall;
5. Coming Up; 6. It's Only Rock 'n' Roll;
7. Don't Tell Me; 8. Addicted To Love; 9. Too
Funky; 10. Rio; 11. Turn Off The Light; 12. Side;
13. F.E.A.R. 14. I'm Real; 15. Street Spirit; 16. Take
My Breath Away; 17. Where The Streets Have No
Name; 18. Number One by Playgroup; 19. Live
Forever; 20. Where's Your Head At; 21. Aerosmith
and Run DMC; 22. Virtual Insanity; 23. Frontier
Psychiatrist; 24. Noddy Holder of Slade; 25. Paul
McCartney & Michael Jackson; 26. Ashes To Ashes;
27. Chevvy Chase; 28. Toni Basil; 29. Chant No.1;
30. Chain Reaction.

WE'RE SO PRETTY, OH SO PRETTY

IT'S hard to believe ... but this year, Punk Rock celebrated its 25th birthday. The genre produced some of the most exciting and volatile records in pop history.

How good is your memory on the days of the bin-liner frock and the pogo dance?

1. WHO recorded the 1982 hit album, Combat Rock?

2. WHICH member of The Damned once starred in a television commercial for Weetabix?

3. AND what was the title of his No.1 solo hit from 1982?

4. NAME the clothes shop in Kings Road, London which was the birthplace of The Sex Pistols.

5. WHO owned the shop?

6. JET Black is the drummer for which successful punk act?

7. WHICH punk superstar once fronted a group named Bazooka Joe?

8. NAME the influential Manchester group who released the Spiral Scratch EP.

9. PAUL Weller fronted The Jam ... but can you name the other two band members?

10. WHICH famous villain made a record called No One Is Innocent with The Sex Pistols?

Answers on Page 82

11. POLY Styrene was the singer with which punk act?

12. NAME the legendary New York club venue which helped launch bands such as Television, Talking Heads and Patti Smith?

13. WHICH New York punk act's famous chant was: "Gabba Gabba Hey"?

14. AND still in the Big Apple, who was the sexy female punk star who once earned a living as a Bunny Girl?

15. WILLIAM Michael Albert Broad bleached his hair blond and became a punk. By what name is he better known?

16. WHICH legendary act made their debut at a punk festival in London's 100 Club performing a 20-minute long version of The Lord's Prayer?

17. WHO was the then unknown punk superstar who played drums with them?

18. NAME the punk rockers who had smash hits in 1978 with If The Kids Are United and Hurry Up Harry.

19. WHAT was the name of the group formed by Johnny Rotten after he quit The Sex Pistols?

20. AND which ex-Pistol launched a new band called The Rich Kids?

Answers on Page 82

21. THEIR singer was a well-know Scot. Name him.

22. WHAT was the title of the influential punk fanzine edited by Mark P?

23. WHO were the record labels who sacked The Sex Pistols before they were signed by Richard Branson to Virgin?

24. NAME the seminal punk label which was home to Ian Dury, The Damned and Wreckless Eric.

25. WHEN Declan McManus changed his name he became a new wave star. Who was he?

26. WHICH outrageous US act released the classic 1977 single, White Punks On Dope?

27. CAN you remember the punk singer who made her acting debut in the controversial Derek Jarman movie, Jubilee?

28. WHICH veteran US star is called ... The Godfather of Punk?

29. IN October 1976, who released what is regarded as the first UK punk single, New Rose?

30. WHO scored a Top Ten UK hit single with Babylon's Burning?

Answers on Page 82

WE'RE SO PRETTY ...
OH SO PRETTY VACANT

ANSWERS:

1. The Clash; 2. Captain Sensible; 3. Happy Talk;
4. Sex; 5. Malcolm McLaren and Vivienne
Westwood; 6. The Stranglers; 7. Adam Ant;
8. Buzzcocks; 9. Bruce Foxton & Rick Buckler;
10. Ronald Biggs; 11. X-Ray Spex; 12. CBGBs;
13. The Ramones; 14. Debbie Harry of Blondie;
15. Billy Idol; 16. Siouxsie and the Banshees; 17. Sid
Vicious; 18. Sham 69; 19. Public Image Limited;
20. Glen Matlock; 21. Midge Ure; 22. Sniffin' Glue;
23. EMI and A & M; 24. Stiff Records; 25. Elvis
Costello; 26. The Tubes; 27. Toyah; 28. Iggy Pop;
29. The Damned; 30. The Ruts.

OR FIND MYSELF
A ROCK AND
ROLL BAND...

GUITAR, bass, keyboards and drums - they're all you need for the perfect rock band. But what do you really know about the musicians who provide the backing to some our most famous singers.

This one's for the boys in the band.

GUITAR:

1. IN which US rock megaband did Slash play lead?

2. WHO was the guitarist in Sixties super group Cream?

3. THE guitarist of Toploader wed Scots TV presenter Gail Porter this summer. Name him?

4. RICHIE Sambora provides the licks for one of rock's most famous bands. Who are they?

5. NAME the guitar legend who played with The Stone Roses.

Answers on Page 88

BASS:

1. JOHN Paul Jones was bassist with which act?

2. NAME the cross-dressing bass player of The Manic Street Preachers.

3. IN Queen, he was the "quiet one". Who was he?

4. WHICH famous bassist fronted Irish rockers Thin Lizzy?

5. WHO plays bass for Travis?

Answers on Page 88

KEYBOARDS:

1. RICK Wakeman starred on keyboards for which legendary rock act?

2. WHO tinkled the ivories for hit band Squeeze?

3. DURAN Duran have notched up 20 years in the business. Who is their keyboard player?

4. NEIL Tennant sings with The Pet Shop Boys ... but who is his sidekick?

5. WHO played keyboards for Seventies super stars, Abba?

Answers on Page 88

DRUMS:

1. BUTCH Vig plays drums for which top US group?

2. THERE were only three members of the Jimi Hendrix Experience – who was the drummer?

3. IN The Eagles, he can sing and drum at the same time. Who is he?

4. NAME the sexy female drummer from Prince's backing group?

5. WHO was drummer with US punk stars Blondie?

Answers on Page 88

OR FIND MYSELF A ROCK AND ROLL BAND ...

ANSWERS:

GUITAR: 1. Guns 'n' Roses; 2. Eric Clapton;
3. Dan Hipgrave; 4. Bon Jovi;
5. John Squire.

BASS: 1. Led Zeppelin; 2. Nicky Wire;
3. John Deacon; 4. Phil Lynott;
5. Dougie Payne.

KEYBOARDS: 1. Yes; 2. Jools Holland; 3. Nick
Rhodes; 4. Chris Lowe; 5. Benny
Andersson.

DRUMS: 1. Garbage; 2. Mitch Mitchell;
3. Don Henley; 4. Sheila E;
5. Clem Burke.

I WRITE
THE SONGS

A HOST of very famous names are
behind some of our best-loved songs.
But as you sing along ... do you know
who penned the track?

Name the composers of these hit songs.

1. ROB Davies co-wrote Kylie Minogue's No.1, Can't Get You Out Of My Head. Which hit Seventies group was he a member of?

2. WHO penned Manic Monday for US girl band, The Bangles?

3. DO They Know It's Christmas? by Band Aid raised millions for famine relief. Who wrote the song?

4. WHICH US country music legend penned Crazy for singer Patsy Cline?

5. NAME the Beach Boy who won a Grammy for I Write The Songs ... a hit in 1976 for Barry Manilow.

6. SCOTS pop act Marmalade had a No.1 in 1968 with Ob-La-Di Ob-La-Da. Which music legends composed it?

7. WHO wrote I'm A Believer for The Monkees?

8. WHICH Scots pop legend penned I Don't Wanna Fight for Tina Turner?

9. AND talking of Tina, name the Scot who wrote her worldwide smash, What's Love Got To Do With It?

10. MARY Hopkins burst on to the UK pop scene in 1969 with the No.1 hit, Those Were The Days. Who wrote it?

Answers on Page 92

11. THE Pretenders scored their first ever hit in 1979 with Stop Your Sobbing. Who composed it?

12. DAVID Bowie recorded China Girl for his album Let's Dance. An old mate wrote it ... who was he?

13. WHICH ex-member of The Waterboys penned She's The One which was a monster hit for Robbie Williams?

14. NAME the famous Scot who wrote Stuck In The Middle With You – covered in 2001 by Louise.

15. WHO was the US country star who wrote the classic I Will Always Love You, which was recorded by Whitney Houston?

16. THIS Scots pair penned Sailing, which became a massive hit when Rod Stewart covered it. Who are they?

17.. WHICH supergroup wrote Islands In The Stream for Kenny Rogers and Dolly Parton in 1983?

18. WHICH star co-wrote Justify My Love with Madonna?

19.. ROXY Music achieved their only UK No.1 single in 1981 with Jealous Guy. They recorded it as a tribute to its writer ... who was he?

20. IN the 1960s, John Fogerty of Creedence Clearwater Revival wrote a song which became one of Status Quo's biggest hits. Name it.

Answers on Page 92

I WRITE THE SONGS

1. Mud; 2. Prince; 3. Midge Ure & Bob Geldof;
4. Willie Nelson; 5. Bruce Johnston; 6. Lennon-
McCartney; 7. Neil Diamond; 8. Lulu; 9. Graham
Lyle; 10. Paul McCartney; 11. Ray Davies; 12. Iggy
Pop; 13. Karl Wallinger; 14. Gerry Rafferty;
15. Dolly Parton; 16. The Sutherland Brothers;
17. The Bee Gees; 18. Lenny Kravitz; 19. John
Lennon; 20. Rockin' All Over The World.

SATURDAY NIGHT AT THE MOVIES

MANY pop stars have been desperate to make it in the movies – some with more success than others. What happens when the worlds of music and film collide?

Test your knowledge on this little lot.

1.   LIONEL Richie won an Oscar in 1985 for the theme song to the movie, White Nights. What was it called?

2.   HOLD Me Thrill Me Kiss Me Kill Me was written for the soundtrack of the Batman movie in 1995. By whom?

3..   WHO starred in the Nick Roeg sci-fi movie, The Man Who Fell To Earth?

4.   WHICH part did he play?

5.   IN which film did Sean Lennon appear alongside Michael Jackson?

6.   WHO composed the soundtrack to the Robert Duvall-Ally McCoist movie, A Shot At Glory?

7..   SIMPLE Minds notched up their only US No.1 single with the theme song from The Breakfast Club. Name it.

8.   WHICH Steve Harley and Cockney Rebel track was used in the film The Full Monty?

9..   GERI Halliwell had a hit song from the soundtrack of Bridget Jones' Diary. Remember what it was called?

10.   WHICH sexy US punk star played opposite actor James Woods in the bizarre film, Videodrome?

Answers on Page 98

11. WHO duetted on the song Come What May from the soundtrack of Moulin Rouge?

12. WHICH cartoon band released a single titled Clint Eastwood?

13. NAME the Bon Jovi hit used in the movie Young Guns.

14. HOLLYWOOD actor Christopher Walken danced through a deserted hotel in the award-winning video for which 2001 single?

15. IN which box office blockbuster was My Heart Will Go On by Celine Dion featured?

16. WHAT was the All Saints' track used in the sound track of the Leonardo di Caprio film, The Beach?

17. DURAN Duran take their name from a character in which futuristic film?

18. WHICH pop cult movie starred Patsy Kensit as Crepe Suzette?

19. WHO was the punk rocker who starred with Harvey Keitel in the chilling film Order Of Death?

20. WHICH song from Robin Hood: Prince Of Thieves topped the UK charts for a record 16 weeks?

Answers on Page 98

21. NAME the James Bond theme song recorded by Scots star Shirley Manson and her group Garbage.

22. AND on the subject of 007, which boy trio had a hit with the Bond song The Living Daylights?

23. WHAT was the classic Iggy Pop song used in the opening sequence of Trainspotting?

24. WHICH actor took the lead role in the bio-pic of Jim Morrison of The Doors?

25. CAN you remember the title of the offbeat movie about The Sex Pistols made by Malcolm McLaren?

26. WHO played a notorious Australian robber in the movie Ned Kelly?

27.. WHAT was the title of The Beatles' first film?

28. WHICH respected actor played the role of Kate Bush's dad in the video for her single, Cloudbusting?

29. IN 1973, which US superstar appeared in the Sam Peckinpah western, Pat Garrett And Billy The Kid?

30. SLADE rode through the streets of Glasgow in 1974 – in an open topped bus – to launch their first movie. What was it called?

Answers on Page 98

SATURDAY NIGHT AT THE MOVIES

ANSWERS:

1. Say You Say Me; 2. U2; 3. David Bowie;
4. Thomas Jerome Newton; 5. Moonwalker;
6. Mark Knopfler; 7. Don't You (Forget About Me);
8. Make Me Smile (Come Up And See Me); 9. It's
Raining Men; 10. Debbie Harry; 11. Ewan
McGregor & Nicole Kidman; 12. Gorillaz; 13. Blaze
of Glory; 14. Weapon of Choice by The Fat Boy
Slim; 15. Titanic; 16. Pure Shores; 17. Barbarella;
18. Absolute Beginners; 19. Johnny Rotten;
20. (Everything I Do) I Do It For You by Bryan
Adams; 21. The World Is Not Enough; 22. A-Ha;
23. Lust For Life; 24. Val Kilmer; 25. The Great
Rock 'n' Roll Swindle; 26. Mick Jagger; 27. A Hard
Day's Night; 28. Donald Sutherland; 29. Bob
Dylan; 30. Slade In Flame.

TV IS KING ....

WE'VE had soap stars making records ... pop stars being paid millions for TV commercials ... and singers trying – and usually failing miserably – to make it on screen.

Try your luck at this combination of TV and pop

1.. NAME the member of Bruce Springsteen's E Street Band who appears in the Channel 4 gangster series, The Sopranos.

2. WHICH ex-punk once played a baddie opposite Edward Woodward in the US drama, The Enforcer?

3. WHO sings the theme song for the BBC TV series, Down To Earth?

4. SINGER Sophie Ellis-Bextor's mother used to present which popular kids' TV show?

5. WHICH glam rock star did a unrehearsed duet with his mate David Bowie on his Seventies' TV show?

6. WHICH actor turned pop singer wrote and starred in Crocodile Shoes?

7. WHO was the member of Mari Wilson's backing group who became an EastEnders' star?

8. WHICH former TV 'tec had a No. 1 hit in 1975 with If?

9. NAME the Edinburgh group whose 1994 No.1 single, Inside, is the theme song for Sky TV's Scottish football coverage?

10. WHICH member of The Monkees starred in the kids' series, Circus Boy?

Answers on Page 104

11. AND which Monkee played Ena Sharples' grandson in Coronation Street?

12. WHICH Sixties singing star now presents TV's Blind Date?

13. NAME the Ben E. King hit used as the theme for a Levi's denim commercial.

14. AND which sexy model turned pop singer stripped down to his boxer shorts in another Levi's ad?

15. WHICH TV star is the "voice" of Bob the Builder?

16. WHO was the Beatle who narrated Thomas the Tank Engine?

17. DAVID Cassidy appeared with his step mum Shirley Jones in which US TV series?

18. IN 2001, which member of The Spice Girls hosted a new talent show for ITV?

19. WHICH ITV newscaster won a Celebrity Stars In Their Eyes as Peggy Lee singing Fever?

20. WHO was the Coronation Street character who portrayed Posh Spice in a Celebrity Stars In Their Eyes?

Answers on Page 104

21. IN 2000, which former Phantom of the Opera appeared as an extra ordering a pint in the Rovers Return?

22. AND still on Corrie ... which UK pop legend went on a diet after character Minnie Caldwell called him "chubby" during an episode of the TV soap?

23. NAME the Aussie soap which once starred Kylie Minogue and Jason Donovan.

24. WHO was the TV news presenter who achieved notoriety when he encouraged The Sex Pistols to swear on his show in 1977?

25. WHICH legendary Scots rock singer played hardman Jake McQuillan in Peter MacDougall's TV drama, Just A Boy's Game?

26. WHO is the brains behind those cuddly TV stars The Wombles?

27. NAME the classic 1980s Friday night rock show hosted by Jools Holland and Paula Yates.

28. IN which UK city was the first edition of Top Of The Pops filmed?

29. WHO stormed off BBC 2's Late Review show when the power failed during their live appearance?

30. IN 1984, Joe Fagin has a Top 10 hit with That's Livin' Alright. It was the theme of which TV drama?

Answers on Page 104

TV IS KING

ANSWERS:

1. Miami Steve van Zandt; 2. Adam Ant; 3. Tony Hadley of Spandau Ballet; 4. Blue Peter; 5. Marc Bolan on the show, Marc; 6. Jimmy Nail; 7. Michelle Collins; 8. Kojak star Telly Savalas; 9. Stiltskin; 10. Mickey Dolenz; 11. Davy Jones; 12. Cilla Black; 13. Stand By Me; 14. Nick Kamen; 15. Neil Morrissey; 16. Ringo Starr; 17. The Partridge Family; 18. Mel B; 19. Kirsty Young; 20. Leanne Battersby; 21. Michael Crawford; 22. Cliff Richard; 23. Neighbours; 24. Bill Grundy; 25. Frankie Miller; 26. Mike Batt; 27. The Tube; 28. Manchester; 29. The Stone Roses; 30. Auf Wiedersehen, Pet.

WE ARE FAMILY ...

SOME of pop's biggest acts have been real family affairs. From the battling Gallagher brothers in Oasis ... to the legendary Osmond clan. Fathers singing with daughters, sisters duetting with brothers - we've had them all.

How much do you know about these famous music families?

1. WHICH family act had Seventies' hits with Close To You and Yesterday Once More?

2. WHO were the brother-sister who hit the charts in 1974 with I'm Leaving It All Up To You?

3. NAME the family act formed by Deniece, Doris, Stedman, Lorraine and Delroy Pearson.

4. WHO were the US country supergroup formed by mum Naomi and daughters Wynonna and Ashley?

5. SHE'S one of Scotland's best-loved female singers ... he's lead singer of The Trash Can Sinatras. Who are they?

6. NAME the country music legend who is the father of singer Carlene Carter.

7. WHICH father-daughter double act had a hit single in 1967 with Somethin' Stupid?

8. THE daughter of Hollywood legend Judy Garland had a hit with Losing My Mind in 1989. Who is she?

9. IN 1995, which legendary sister and brother recorded Scream?

10. HE first cracked the UK charts in 1958 with Endless Sleep ... but today he's better known as which pop star's dad?

Answers on Page 108

WE ARE FAMILY

1. The Carpenters;

2. Donny & Marie Osmond;

3. Five Star;

4. The Judds;

5. Eddi and Frank Reader;

6. Johnny Cash;

7. Frank & Nancy Sinatra;

8. Liza Minnelli;

9. Janet & Michael Jackson;

10. Marti Wilde, father of Kim Wilde.

HE AIN'T HEAVY, HE'S MY BROTHER

Many top acts have featured two or more brothers in the line up. Or maybe someone followed a brother into the music world. Ask your bro to help with this selection.

Name these showbiz siblings ...

1. WHICH New Zealand-born brothers formed Crowded House?

2. NAME the brothers in The Kinks.

3. PAT and Greg Kane are better known as which act?

4. WHO are the siblings in the current Radiohead line-up.

5. NAME the twins who are better known as The Proclaimers.

6. BROS hit No.1 in 1988 with I Owe You Nothing. Name the brothers who fronted the group.

7. MIKE McGear of The Scaffold is the brother of which superstar?

8. THE brother of a former New Kids On The Block member starred in the movie Boogie Nights. Who is he?

9. NAME the Scots brothers in AC/DC?

10. WHO were the influential Eighties band formed by Paddy and Martin McAloon?

Answers on Page 112

HE AIN'T HEAVY, HE'S MY BROTHER

ANSWERS:

1. Neil & Tim Finn;

2. Ray & Dave Davies;

3. Hue And Cry;

4. Jonny & Colin Greenwood;

5. Craig & Charlie Reid;

6. Luke & Matt Goss;

7. Paul McCartney;

8. Mark Wahlberg, brother of New Kids' star Donnie;

9. Malcolm & Angus Young;

10. Prefab Sprout.

SISTERS ARE DOING IT FOR THEMSELVES

Girls, too, are hitting the heights together. But do you know your sister acts?

Sisters, sisters .... Who are they?

1. BY what name are Andrea, Sharon and Caroline better known?

2. NAME the sisters who formed Eternal.

3. WHICH sisters had a No.1 hit in 1987 with Respectable?

4. WHO were the sexy sisters in All Saints?

5. WHICH sister act were "in the mood for dancing" in 1979?

6. NAME the sisters in Sister Sledge.

7. WHICH US sisters had hits with Slowhand and Automatic?

8. WHO are the chart-topping Irish vocal act which features Adele and Keavy Lynch?

9.. WENDY and Carnie Wilson formed the US band Wilson Phillips. Who is their legendary dad?

10. NAME the US country music star who is the sister of singer Crystal Gayle?

Answers on Page 116

SISTERS ARE DOING IT FOR THEMSELVES

ANSWERS:

1. The Corrs;

2. Easther & Vernett Benett;

3. Mel & Kim;

4. Natalie & Nicole Appleton;

5. The Nolans;

6. Kathie, Debra, Joan & Kim Sledge;

7. The Pointer Sisters;

8. B*Witched;

9. Ex-Beach Boy, Brian Wilson;

10. Loretta Lynn.

SISTERS ARE DOING
IT FOR THEMSELVES

WE'LL BRING THE HOUSE DOWN

IN the Seventies, a top music magazine conducted a poll to find the best gig in Britain. The verdict was unanimous ... the famous Glasgow Apollo. Dozens of top acts - including The Who, Roxy Music and David Bowie - all hailed the former cinema as the most celebrated rock venue in Europe.

What do you remember about the glory days of the Apollo?

1. WHICH Irish legend is reported to have suffered an attack of vertigo on the 20ft high Apollo stage?

2. NAME the supergroup who supported Mott The Hoople at the venue in 1973.

3. AND who opened for Neil Young & Crazy Horse later that same year?

4. WHICH Scots artist was awarded a silver replica of an Apollo seat for playing to 33,117 people in 12 days?

5. IN 1977, who shocked Glasgow city councillors when they brought on sexy female strippers during their hit song, Nice 'n' Sleazy?

6. NAME the Glasgow group who sold out the Apollo despite not having a record deal.

7. WHICH shock rocker did Mary Whitehouse try to ban from appearing at the venue in 1972?

8. WHAT was the 4,200 capacity cinema called when it opened in 1927?

9. DURING one gig a group of technicians calculated that the balcony dipped by 12 inches. Which band was on stage?

10. WHO opened for electro-pop star Gary Numan when he made his Apollo debut in September 1979?

Answers on Page 122

118

11. WHICH act recorded an EP called Dig The New Breed at the venue in 1982?

12. COMPLETE the Apollo's famous advertising slogan: They've All Been ... And ****** *** ****** ****.

13. NAME the solo star who opened his show by walking through the front stalls – and climbing up a ladder on to the stage.

14. WHAT was the collective name of the show headlined by Ian Dury, Elvis Costello, Wreckless Eric, Larry Wallis and Nick Lowe in 1977?

15. IN May 1976, The Rolling Stones played three sell-out gigs at the venue. What other big event was staged in the city in that week?

16. WHO played four gigs as part of his epic Stage tour in 1978?

17. THE previous year, The Jacksons pulled out of a show at just 45 minutes notice. Why?

18. WHO headlined a Hogmanay gig broadcast live on BBC 2's Whistle Test in 1979?

19. WHICH Scots supergroup played their debut gig in Satellite City – the dance hall upstairs – on January 17, 1978?

20. IN June 1980, Paul McCartney rocketed up the US charts with a song recorded live at the Apollo the previous December. What was it called?

Answers on Page 122

21. WHAT was the name given to the posh "double" seats in the balcony which were a favourite of courting couples when the venue operated as a cinema?

22. CAN you remember the famous slogan printed on the carpet during those days?

23. SHOWBIZ entrepreneur Frank Lynch's company owned the Apollo. What were they called?

24. WHO taped three gigs at the venue in October 1976 for a brilliant live album?

25. WHICH US country music legend played the first gig at the Apollo in September 1973?

26. WHO was the Scots singer who appeared at what was billed as the final gig on July 5, 1978?

27. AFTER the venue re-opened ... which act brought the curtain down for the final time in June 1985?

28. WHICH legendary Scots band played three Christmas shows at the venue in 1975?

29. IN 1973, Slade played a gig with two support acts who went on to greater things. Name them.

30. WHEN did The Sex Pistols headline the venue?

Answers on Page 122

WE'LL BRING THE HOUSE DOWN

ANSWERS:

1. Van Morrison; 2. Queen; 3. The Eagles; 4. Billy Connolly; 5. The Stranglers; 6. Scheme; 7. Alice Cooper; 8. Green's Playhouse; 9. Status Quo; 10. Orchestral Manoeuvres in the Dark; 11. The Jam; 12. "They're all coming back"; 13. Peter Gabriel; 14. Stiffs Greatest Stiffs; 15. The European Cup Final between Bayern Munich and St Etienne at Hampden Park; 16. David Bowie; 17. Michael Jackson took ill; 18. Blondie; 19. Simple Minds; 20. Coming Up; 21. The golden divans; 22. "It's good ... It's Green's"; 23. Unicorn Leisure; 24. Status Quo; 25. Johnny Cash; 26. Christian; 27. The Style Council; 28. The Sensational Alex Harvey Band; 29. Suzi Quatro & Thin Lizzy; 30. They didn't ... their 1977 gig was banned by the local council.

CALL ME NUMBER ONE

IT'S every artist's dream to hit No.1 in the singles charts. Some lucky acts top the charts time after time ... while others only manage one No.1 single in a lifelong career.

Can you remember who hit the top spot with these singles?

1960s:

1. WHICH Don and Phil had a No. 1 with Cathy's Clown?

2. WHO were Shakin' All Over?

3. NAME the singer who had to tell Laura he loved her.

4. WHO became a star with the song Runaway?

5. WHICH singer and his backing group performed the theme song to the movie, The Young Ones?

6. WHO had a futuristic chart topper with Telstar.

7. WHO gave a letter to the postman ... but it was returned to sender?

8. WHICH Merseybeat act sang Sweets For My Sweet?

9. YOU'LL Never Walk Alone has been adopted by Celtic fans ... who had a No.1 hit with the song?

10. WHO hit No.1 twice in 1963 with She Loves You?

Answers on Page 128

11. WHICH London act were Glad All Over the following year?

12. NAME the vocal duo who had a No.1 with A World Without Love.

13. DO Wah Diddy Diddy topped the charts in 1964. Who recorded it?

14. WHICH barefoot star recorded (There's) Always Something There To Remind Me?

15. WHO were Tired Of Waiting For You?

16. WHICH UK superstar scored his first No.1 with It's Not Unusual?

17. NAME the 1965 No.1 hit for Unit Four Plus Two.

18. BOB Dylan wrote Mr Tambourine Man. But which band had a UK No.1 hit with the song?

19. WHO heard the sound of Distant Drums in 1966?

20. WHICH UK piano man recorded The Ballad of Bonnie and Clyde?

Answers on Page 128

1970s

1. WHO scored their only No.1 hit with Love Grows (Where My Rosemary Goes)?

2. BACK Home was a chart topper for which sports squad?

3. WHICH female star had a Band Of Gold in 1970?

4. NAME the Dad's Army cast member who topped the charts with Grandad.

5. WHICH vocal act sang Hey Girl Don't Bother Me?

6. IN 1972, who caused outrage with the song, School's Out?

7. WHO made some Mouldy Old Dough when they hit No.1 in 1972?

8. WHICH glam band hit No.1 with Blockbuster the following year?

9. WHO were the male-female duo who recorded Welcome Home?

10. THE instrumental Eye Level was a hit for which act?

Answers on Page 128

11. WHO sang Billy Don't Be A Hero?

12. THIS gravel voiced French star topped the charts with She. Who is he?

13. WHAT was the Christmas No.1 in 1974?

14. NAME the Scots pop supergroup who scored a No.1 with Bye Bye Baby.

15. AND still with the Scots ... who was top of the pops with D.I.V.O.R.C.E.?

16. WHO had a No.1 hit in 1976 with No Charge?

17. WHICH UK act topped the charts with So You Win Again?

18. TUBEWAY Army had a smash hit in 1979 with which pioneering pop song?

19. VIDEO Killed The Radio Star according to which group?

20. WHO were Walking On The Moon in 1979?

Answers on Page 128

CALL ME NO.1

THE 1960s

ANSWERS:

1. The Everly Brothers; 2. Johnny Kidd & the Pirates; 3. Ricky Valance; 4. Del Shannon; 5. Cliff Richard & the Shadows; 6. The Tornados; 7. Elvis Presley; 8. The Searchers; 9. Gerry & the Pacemakers; 10. The Beatles; 11. The Dave Clark Five; 12. Peter & Gordon; 13. Manfred Mann; 14. Sandie Shaw; 15. The Kinks; 16. Tom Jones; 17. Concrete And Clay; 18. The Byrds; 19. Jim Reeves; 20. Georgie Fame.

The 1970s

ANSWERS:

1. Edison Lighthouse; 2. England's World Cup Squad; 3. Freda Payne; 4. Clive Dunn; 5. The Tams; 6. Alice Cooper; 7. Lieutenant Pigeon; 8. The Sweet; 9. Peters & Lee; 10. The Simon Park Orchestra; 11. Paper Lace; 12. Charles Aznavour; 13. Lonely This Christmas by Mud; 14. The Bay City Rollers; 15. Billy Connolly; 16. JJ Barrie; 17. Hot Chocolate; 18. Are Friends Electric; 19. The Buggles; 20. The Police.

1980s

1. WHO had Brass In Pocket in 1980?

2. NAME the Dexy's Midnight Runners No.1 from May, 1980.

3. BY what name was Suicide Is Painless better known?

4. WHICH UK star had two posthumous No.1 hits in 1981?

5. IN the same year Roxy Music notched up their only UK No.1 single with another of his compositions. What was it?

6. WHICH group of kids recorded the dreaded There's No One Quite Like Grandma?

7. WHAT record kept Vienna by Ultravox off the No.1 position in 1981?

8. WHO were in the Land Of Make Believe?

9. NAME the Scots star who scored a No.1 with Japanese Boy?

10. NAME the pretty boy group who were Too Shy.

Answers on Page 134

11. ROD Stewart headlined Ibrox Stadium in the summer of 1983 after he'd just hit No.1. What was the song?

12. WHO toasted their chart-topping success in 1983 with some Red Red Wine?

13. DURAN Duran got to No.1 with which song in 1984?

14. WHAT was the historic Christmas No.1 later that year?

15. WHO guested on harmonica on the 1985 Eurythmics' hit, There Must Be An Angel (Playing With My Heart)?

16. WHICH superstar got Into The Groove?

17. NAME the comedy act who reached No.1 with The Chicken Song.

18. IN 1987, another comedy group – The Firm – topped the charts with a song inspired by a TV sci-fi show. What was it called?

19. WHO were Doctorin' The Tardis in 1988?

20. WHICH Scots supergroup had their only UK No.1 single with Belfast Child in 1989?

Answers on Page 134

1990s

1. WHAT was the first UK No.1 of the new decade?

2. SINEAD O'Connor had her only No.1 single with Nothing Compares 2 U. Who wrote it?

3. WHO shot to the top of the charts with Itsy Bitsy Teeny Weeny Yellow Polka Dot Bikini?

4. WHICH heavy metal anthem knocked Saviour's Day by Cliff Richard off the top of the charts?

5. NAME the punk act who said ... Should I Stay Or Should I Go.

6. WHO was the TV comic who fronted The Wonder Stuff on Dizzy?

7. WHICH superstars duetted on Don't Let The Sun Go Down On Me?

8. WHO were Deeply Dippy?

9. CHARLES and Eddie hit No.1 with a classic song ... then vanished without trace. What was its title?

10. WHO hit No.1 with the Abba-Esque EP?

Answers on Page 134

11. WHICH Scots pop legend joined Take That on Relight My Fire?

12. THE 1994 No.1 single, Things Can Only Get Better was adopted by the Labour Party during a General Election. Who recorded it?

13. WHO was Boombastic?

14. NAME the Christmas No.1 in 1995.

15. BABYLON Zoo topped the charts with Spaceman. Who was their singer?

16. WHICH group enjoyed Breakfast At Tiffanys in 1996?

17. TWO acts teamed up on I Wanna Be The Only One ... name them.

18. WHO had a Brimful Of Asha in 1998?

19. WHICH US punk act scored a chart topping UK comeback in 1999 with Maria?

20. WHAT was the last UK No.1 in 1999 before we celebrated the new Millenium?

Answers on Page 134

CALL ME NO.1

ANSWERS:

1980s

1. The Pretenders; 2. Geno; 3. The Theme From M*A*S*H; 4. John Lennon; 5. Jealous Guy; 6. St. Winifred's School Choir; 7. Shaddup You Face by Joe Dolce; 8. Bucks Fizz; 9. Aneka; 10. Kajagoogoo; 11. Baby Jane; 12. UB40; 13. The Reflex; 14. Do They Know It's Christmas? by Band Aid; 15. Stevie Wonder; 16. Madonna; 17. Spitting Image; 18. Star Trekkin'; 19. The Timelords; 20. Simple Minds.

1990s

1. Hangin' Tough by New Kids On The Block; 2. Prince; 3. Bombalurina; 4. Bring Your Daughter To The Slaughter by Iron Maiden; 5. The Clash; 6. Vic Reeves; 7. Elton John & George Michael; 8. Right Said Fred; 9. Would I Lie To You; 10. Erasure; 11. Lulu; 12. D:Ream; 13. Shaggy; 14. Earth Song by Michael Jackson; 15. Jas Mann; 16. Deep Blue Something; 17. Eternal & Be Be Winans; 18. Cornershop; 19. Blondie; 20. I Have A Dream/Seasons In The Sun by Westlife.

YOU'RE SUCH A LOVELY AUDIENCE ...

FOR millions of music fans, the Beatles are the most innovative pop act of all time. Their amazing songs – from their debut single, Love Me Do to their final studio album, Let It Be – have influenced scores of other bands.

But just how good is your knowledge of the life and career of John, Paul, George and Ringo?

1.   IN 1957, Paul McCartney auditioned for John Lennon's group. What were they called?

2.   WHERE did the audition take place?

3.   WHO was the Beatles' original bass player?

4.   AND name the drummer who was replaced in the line-up by Ringo Starr?

5.   THE group learned their craft with a residency in the Indra Club. In which German city was it located?

6.   ASTRID Kirchherr can claim to have "invented" what vital part of the group's distinctive look?

7.   WHICH member of the group was deported from Germany by the authorities for being under age?

8.   THE manager of the North End Music Store in Liverpool went to see the group play in a local club ... before deciding to sign them up. Name him.

9.   WHAT was the name of the legendary club in Matthews Street?

10.   WHICH top record label turned The Beatles down saying: "Guitar groups are on their way out"?

Answers on Page 142

11. WHAT is Scots drummer Andy White's famous claim to fame?

12. WHAT chart position did the group's debut single achieve in 1962?

13. NAME the BBC engineer who became the band's lifelong producer.

14. WHICH song gave John, Paul, George and Ringo their first UK No.1 hit?

15. IN 1964, The Beatles made their debut on which famous American television variety series?

16. LENNON and McCartney wrote the song which gave rivals The Rolling Stones their second big hit in 1963. What was it called?

17. WHICH cast member from the BBC comedy series Steptoe And Son appeared in the group's first film, A Hard Day's Night?

18. WHY did the Fab Four visit Buckingham Palace in 1965?

19. THAT same year, their first double A-sided single hit No.1. What were the song titles?

20. IN 1966, why did thousands of fans in America burn their Beatle records?

Answers on Page 142

21. WHAT happened on August 29, 1966?

22. WHERE did it take place?

23. WHICH smoochy record kept the classic Penny Lane/Strawberry Fields Forever off the No.1 spot in 1967?

24. WHO was the ex-world heavyweight boxing champ who appeared on the montage sleeve of Sergeant Pepper's Lonely Hearts Club Band?

25. WHICH song on the album was inspired by a newspaper clipping read by Lennon which told of holes in the roads in Lancashire?

26. WHY can't fans hear the last notes on the landmark Pepper LP?

27. NAME the ill-fated Beatles' movie which featured the eggmen and the walrus?

28. IN 1968, the group launched their own multi-media company. What did they call it?

29. THEY signed a US songwriter to the label – who later married Carly Simon. Who was he?

30. WHAT was the title of the animated Beatle film which featured baddies, The Blue Meanies?

Answers on Page 142

31. BY what name did the innovative double album released in 1968 with just a serial number on the sleeve become known?

32. GEORGE Harrison contributed While My Guitar Gently Weeps to the LP. Who played guitar on the track?

33. WHICH Beatle song did US mass murderer Charles Manson claim drove him to kill?

34. WHERE did the group's last "public" performance take place?

35. ON which famous London street were they?

36. WHAT was unusual about The Beatles' last ever UK No.1 single Ballad of John and Yoko in 1969?

37. WHICH George Harrison composition did Frank Sinatra famously describe as ... "one of the greatest love songs ever written"?

38. WHO was the first member to actually quit the group?

39. IN which famous London art gallery did John Lennon first meet Yoko Ono?

40. WHAT was the title of the last Beatles' movie which clearly showed the group falling apart?

Answers on Page 142

41. IN 1977, a live album was released featuring the band playing at a famous venue in California. Name it.

42. RINGO wed a Bond girl who appeared with Roger Moore in The Spy Who Loved Me. Who is she?

43. WHAT did John and Yoko do at the Amsterdam Hilton Hotel to appeal for world peace?

44. WHICH Beatles related artist had hit singles with Too Late For Goodbyes and Saltwater?

45. IN 1995, Paul, George and Ringo finished off an old Lennon composition and released it as a single. What was it called?

46. WHICH member of ELO produced the song?

47. WHAT was the collective name for the three albums of rarities and out-takes released in 1995-96?

48. WHICH musician and TV host interviewed the surviving Beatles for the accompanying documentary series?

49. NAME the Beatles song Paul McCartney performed at the finale of the UK Live Aid at Wembley Stadium.

50. WHAT was the last unearthed Beatles song to be released as a single in 1996?

Answers on Page 142

YOU'RE SUCH A
LOVELY AUDIENCE ...

ANSWERS:

1. The Quarrymen; 2. A church fete in Woolton,
Liverpool; 3. Stuart Sutcliffe; 4. Pete Best;
5. Hamburg; 6. The Beatle mop-top haircut;
7. George Harrison; 8. Brian Epstein; 9. The
Cavern; 10. Decca Records; 11. He played drums
on Love Me Do; 12. Number 17. 13. George
Martin; 14. From Me To You; 15. The Ed Sullivan
Show; 16. I Wanna Be Your Man; 17. Wilfred
Bramble; 18. They were presented with MBEs by
The Queen; 19. We Can Work It Out/Day Tripper;
20. Because Lennon said in an interview that ...
"We are more popular than Jesus now"; 21. It was
their last ever proper gig; 22. Candlestick Park, San
Francisco; 23. Release Me by Engelbert
Humperdinck; 24. Sonny Liston; 25. A Day In The
Life; 26. An orchestra played a note audible only to
dogs; 27. Magical Mystery Tour; 28. Apple;
29. James Taylor; 30. Yellow Submarine; 31. The
White Album; 32. Eric Clapton; 33. Helter Skelter;
34. On the roof of the Apple offices; 35. 3 Saville
Row; 36. Only John Lennon and Paul McCartney
played on the track; 37. Something; 38. Ringo
Starr ... but he later rejoined; 39. The Indica
Gallery; 40. Let It Be; 41. Live at the Hollywood
Bowl; 42; Barbara Bach; 43. They lay in bed for a
week; 44. Julian Lennon; 45. Free As A Bird;
46. Jeff Lynne; 47. Anthology; 48. Jools Holland;
49. Let It Be; 50. Real Love.

FEED THE WORLD

IN 1984, Bob Geldof sat at home – pinned to his armchair – watching a BBC news report about an impending famine in Ethiopia. The Boomtown Rats star was so moved by what he saw, he phoned mate Midge Ure and said: "We need to try and do something". The rest is history.

Here's a test of your knowledge of that historic event.

1. WHICH artist sung the very first line of the Band Aid single?

2. IN which London studio was the historic song recorded?

3. WHO produced it?

4. NAME the star who sang the line: "But tonight thank God it's them instead of you"?

5. WHICH record was at No.1 in the UK before Band Aid knocked it off the top spot?

6. NAME the colourful pop star who flew home from America just to record his line of lyric.

7. THE cream of America's rock talent was spurred into action by Band Aid. What was the title of their song?

8. AND by what name were the group – formed by Michael Jackson and Lionel Richie – known?

9. WHAT was the date of the historic Live Aid events?

10. NAME the concert venue in the UK.

Answers on Page 148

11. AND where was the show staged in the US?

12. WHICH legendary act opened the show in the UK ... and what was the song?

13. BOB Geldof performed an emotion charged Boomtown Rats hit with his group. What was it?

14. WHO promoted the UK show?

15. HOW were the road crews able to change the sound equipment so quickly between acts?

16. WHICH superstar was able to perform at both Live Aid shows?

17. WHO were the members of the Royal Family who attended the UK event?

18. WHICH UK star deliberately cut his set short by one number ... to make time to screen a harrowing film of famine victims?

19. THE US event actually began a few minutes earlier than scheduled. What happened?

20. WHO then performed the first official number to get the US show under way?

Answers on Page 148

21. WHICH act sang his big hit, Wouldn't It Be Good, at the UK show?

22. NAME the US comic who fulfilled an ambition when he introduced his music heroes The Four Tops and Billy Ocean in the Stateside event.

23. WHO reunited with his old mates Black Sabbath to appear in the US?

24. U2 appeared on stage at the UK show ... but they were introduced from the US by a Hollywood legend. Name him.

25. MEL Smith and Griff Rhys Jones told the UK crowd: "It's Her Majesty ... Queen". What was the first song in the group's amazing set?

26. WHICH Glasgow band flew to the US to appear at the epic concert there?

27. NAME the British supergroup who reformed specially for Live Aid ... and performed a brilliant set which included Love Reign O'er Me.

28. ON which song did Elton John and George Michael duet?

29. IN America, actress Bette Midler had the pleasure of introducing one of her favourite singers. Who was she?

30. WHAT happened when Paul McCartney sat down at the piano to perform Let It Be?

Answers on Page 148

31. AT the end of the UK gig, what did a member of the US organisation ask Bob Geldof? The three-word question became the title of his autobiography.

32. THE Thompson Twins couldn't believe it when a US superstar joined them on backing vocals. Who was she?

33. PHIL Collins played drums with Led Zeppelin stars Robert Plant, Jimmy Page and John Paul Jones ... on which classic song?

34. WHO performed their then current No.1 single – the Bond theme, A View To A Kill – at the US show?

35. MICK Jagger had a very famous backing group in the US when he sang, Just Another Night. Who were they?

36. THEN Mick performed a sex-charged duet on State Of Shock with which female star ... ripping off her skirt in the process?

37. WHICH members of The Rolling Stones joined their buddy Bob Dylan on stage?

38. DURING the US finale – We Are The World – which Bellshill-born female star was part of the on stage ensemble?

39. HOW many people were estimated to have watched Live Aid around the world?

40. AND how much money did both concerts raise?

Answers on Page 148

FEED THE WORLD

1. Paul Young; 2. Sarm West; 3. Trevor Horn;
4. Bono of U2; 5. The Power Of Love by Frankie
Goes To Hollywood; 6. Boy George; 7. We Are The
World; 8. USA for Africa; 9. July 13, 1985;
10. Wembley Stadium, London; 11. JFK Stadium,
Philadelphia; 12. Status Quo with Rockin' All Over
The World; 13. I Don't Like Mondays; 14. Harvey
Goldsmith; 15. They used a revolving stage; 16. Phil
Collins who flew from London to Philadelphia on
Concorde; 17. Prince Charles and Princess Diana;
18. David Bowie; 19. The organisers let a busker
named Bernard Watson – who'd camped outside the
stadium for a week – sing a song; 20. Joan Baez;
21. Nik Kershaw; 22. Chevvy Chase; 23. Ozzy
Osbourne; 24. Jack Nicholson; 25. Bohemian
Rhapsody; 26. Simple Minds; 27. The Who;
28. Don't Let The Sun Go Down On Me;
29. Madonna; 30. His vocal mike packed up; 31. "Is
that it?"; 32. Madonna; 33. Stairway To Heaven;
34. Duran Duran; 35. Hall & Oates; 36. Tina
Turner; 37. Keith Richards & Ronnie Wood;
38. Sheena Easton; 39. 1.5 billion people;
40. £50 million.

I JUST WANT YOU BACK FOR GOOD

TAKE THAT were the biggest male UK pop phenomenon of the 1990s. The five-piece vocal act sold records by the million before they split up.

What do you remember of the hysteria they created?

1. ROBBIE Williams and Gary Barlow are the two most famous members of the group. Who were the other three?

2. WHICH pop manager helped steer the group to stardom?

3. THEIR first chart hit only reached a lowly No.38 in the UK Top 40. What was it called?

4. THEY scored their first Top Ten hit in June, 1992. What was its title?

5. THE song was a cover version ... two acts originally had a hit with it. Who were they?

6. WHO was the oldest member of Take That?

7. AS a child, which group member once backed Ken Dodd on the organ?

8. AND who turned to music after failing to make it as professional footballer following trials with Manchester United?

9. WHICH Take That member had a small part in the TV soap, Brookside?

10. THREE of the lads were in a group before the formation of Take That. What was it called?

Answers on Page 154

11. THEY released a single on their own Dance UK label in July 1991. Remember its title?

12. IN 1992, Take That did a nationwide "Safe Sex" tour. Which health organisation did it support?

13. NAME their 1992 debut album.

14. IN December of that year, the group scooped seven different trophies at which top pop awards?

15. THEY had to wait until 1993 for their first UK No.1 single. Name it.

16. HOW many UK No.1 singles did they have in total?

17. ONE of their most famous hits is Could It Be Magic. Who originally had a hit with it?

18. WHICH product did Take That endorse in the US?

19. WHICH Take That hit featured a guest appearance by Scots singer Lulu?

20. NAME their second album in 1993.

Answers on Page 154

21. IN December 1993, they topped the singles charts with Babe. But who pipped them to the Christmas No.1?

22. WHO wrote their classic hit, Back For Good?

23. WHO was the first member of the group to jump ship and quit the group in 1985?

24. WHEN did the rest of the band announce they were bowing out too?

25. WHAT was their last UK hit single in 1996?

26. WHO was the first member of the group to have a solo hit?

27. ROBBIE Williams launched his solo career with a cover of which George Michael hit?

28. AND Mark Owen opened his chart account with a No.3 solo hit. Name it.

29. WHEN Robbie played Hampden Park in Glasgow last summer he did a joke punk version of which Take That song?

30. AND Robbie had to wait until September 1998 to notch up his first solo UK No.1 single. What was it called?

Answers on Page 154

I JUST WANT YOU BACK FOR GOOD

ANSWERS:

1. Howard Donald, Mark Owen & Jason Orange;
2. Nigel Martin Smith; 3. Promises; 4. It Only Takes A Minute; 5. Jonathan King & Tavares; 6. Howard Donald ... born on April 28, 1968; 7. Gary Barlow; 8. Mark Owen; 9. Robbie Williams; 10. The Cutest Rush; 11. Do What U Like; 12. The Family Planning Association; 13. Take That And Party; 14. Smash Hits Awards; 15. Pray; 16. Eight; 17. Barry Manilow; 18. Breakfast cereal; 19. Relight My Fire; 20. Everything Changes; 21. Mr Blobby with the song, Mr Blobby; 22. Gary Barlow; 23. Robbie Williams; 24. February 1996; 25. How Deep Is Your Love?; 26. Gary Barlow with Forever Love in July 1996; 27. Freedom; 28. Child; 29. Back For Good; 30. Millennium.

I REALLY, REALLY, REALLY WANNA ZIGAZIG-AH

ANYTHING you can do ... we can do better. That was the pop manifesto of The Spice Girls when they exploded on to the UK pop scene in 1996. Mel B, Geri Halliwell, Emma Bunton, Victoria Adams and Mel C preached the gospel of "Girl Power". Their catchy songs and colourful pop image made them the the most successful all-girl act in UK pop history.

But what do you really know about Scary, Ginger, Baby, Posh and Sporty?

1. IN their early days, the girls lived, ate and slept together in a house in an attempt at female bonding. Where was it?

2. NAME the pop manager who signed them up in May 1985 ... and was later sacked.

3. WHAT UK record label snapped up the group in a lucrative albums deal?

4. WHO nicknamed the group members ... Scary, Ginger, Baby, Posh and Sporty?

5. WHAT was the title of their debut single which reached No.1 in July 1996?

6. HOW many UK No.1 singles did The Spice Girls have in total?

7. NAME their only US No.1 single?

8. WHICH group member's past as a former nude model came back to haunt her?

9. IN December 1996, they grabbed the coveted Christmas No.1 single. With which song?

10. THEY signed a big money endorsement deal with soft drink, Pepsi Cola. What track was used on the ad?

Answers on Page 158

11. THE group also appeared in a high-profile advertising campaign for which savoury snack?

12. WHICH high-brow magazine revealed that Geri and Victoria were supporters of the Tory Party?

13. WHO was the politician that the girls claimed launched ... "Girl Power"?

14. NAME the respected British actor who played their manager in the movie, Spiceworld.

15. IN which video did each Spice Girl dress up as a fairy?

16. GERI Halliwell became an ambassador for which global organisation?

17. IN which country were the group touring when they heard the shock news that Geri had quit the group?

18. WHICH Spice Girl was the first to score a solo No.1 single?

19. AND which member of the group released an album titled, Northern Star?

20. WHO is Pheonix Chi?

Answers on Page 158

157

I REALLY, REALLY, REALLY WANNA ... ZIGAZIG-AH

ANSWERS:

1. Maidenhead, Berkshire; 2. Simon Fuller; 3. Virgin Records; 4. Pop magazine, Smash Hits; 5. Wannabe; 6. Eight; 7. Wannabe; 8. Geri Halliwell; 9. 2 Become 1; 10. Step To Me; 11. Walker's Crisps; 12. The Spectator; 13. Margaret Thatcher; 14. Richard E. Grant; 15. Viva Forever; 16. The United Nations; 17. America; 18. Mel B. with I Want You Back in September, 1998; 19. Mel C.; 20. She's Mel B's daughter.

PUMPING ON YOUR STEREO

IF you were stranded on a desert island which album would you want washed up on the beach? Provided you'd managed to salvage a CD player from the ship-wreck, of course. I think I'd choose Abbey Road by The Beatles. All music fans have an album which means something to them.

Test your knowledge on these classic album teasers.

1. WHICH superstar singer made an album of duets with acts such as Catatonia and Heather Small titled Reload?

2. RATTLESNAKES was the 1984 debut album of which successful Scottish group?

3. NAME the classic Roxy Music album which featured Playboy model Marilyn Cole on the sleeve?

4. WHICH Welsh supergroup had Just Enough Education to Perform?

5. AND name their fellow countrymen who released Everything Must Go in 1996?

6. WHAT was the title of Madonna's 1983 debut album?

7. WHICH Seventies heart throb revamped his hit songs for Then And Now in 2001?

8. NAME the US dance act whose latest CD is simply titled ... 8701.

9. AND no messing about either from Bob the Builder ... what was his hit album called?

10. HE'S part Jimi Hendrix, part Prince – and his 1991 CD was titled, Mama Said. Who is he?

Answers on Page 166

11. WHICH Motown legend recorded the masterpiece, Original Musiquarium?

12. IN 1978, this group changed their name from The Hype ... and two years later released their stunning debut album, Boy. Who are they?

13. STREET Fighting Years was a 1989 album release by which Scottish act?

14. NAME the classic album released by Paul Simon in 1986 which featured musicians from South Africa.

15. THE second album by Garbage had a rather unusual title. What was it?

16. WHO released an acoustic live solo album in 2001 called Days Of Speed?

17. AND what was the title of his first group's seminal 1977 debut album?

18. WHO said Welcome To The Pleasuredome in 1984?

19. THE title of The Police's third album in 1980 sounded like pure gibberish. Remember what it was?

20. WHICH singer-songwriter stormed the charts with the CD, White Ladder?

Answers on Page 166

21. NAME the hard-living band who had a hit in 1985 with Rum, Sodomy And The Lash.

22. ALANIS Morissette hit the big time in 1995 with a great record which sold 15 million copies in the US alone. What was it called?

23. WHICH ex-Housemartin released You've Come A Long Way Baby in 1998?

24. WHO scored a worldwide hit with the monster selling Brothers In Arms?

25. WHICH US rock legend compiled a triple album of in-concert appearances titled, Live 1975-85?

26. NAME the influential Scots act who recorded Hats in 1989.

27. KYLIE Minogue's latest smash hit CD is called Fever ... but can you remember the title of her 1988 debut album?

28. NAME the top UK dance act who were Travelling Without Moving?

29. WHO recorded the classic albums Dark Side Of The Moon and The Wall?

30. WHICH ex-punk threw off the safety pins and put on the dandy highwayman gear to become Prince Charming in 1981?

Answers on Page 166

31. NAME the controversial US rap act who released their debut album Licensed To Ill in 1986.

32. THE LP Do It Yourself was released in four different wallpaper design sleeves. Who by?

33. WHICH new group shot to stardom in 2001 with the splendid, Love Is Here?

34. NAME the female solo star who notched up one year in the charts in 2001 with A Day Without Rain.

35. PJ Harvey won the prestigious Mercury Music Award in 2001. What was her album called?

36. WHICH sexy US country star had a smash hit album titled, The Woman In Me?

37. WHO were the American rock act who urged fans to ... Take Off Your Pants And Jacket?

38. WHICH female star enjoyed posthumous chart success with Songbird?

39. THIS respected UK singer-songwriter was in his Imperial Bedroom in 1982. Name him.

40. CAN you remember the title of The Rolling Stones' classic live album of 1970 ... which featured drummer Charlie Watts dancing on the cover?

Answers on Page 166

41. WHO was Lovesexy in 1988?

42. CLIFF Richard has had hits in the 50s, 60s, 70s, 80s and 90s ... and he's still going strong. It all started with an album released in 1959 – name it.

43. WHICH act's 2001 album We Love Life includes the single The Trees?

44. IF you were listening to Kid A on your walkman ... which band would you have in your headphones?

45. WHO released the classic "rock opera" Tommy in 1969?

46. WHICH Scots act are The Invisible Band?

47. IN 1970, a triple album called All Things Must Pass was recorded by which Beatle?

48. GREEN and New Adventures In Hi-Fi were hit albums for which US supergroup?

49. NAME the CD which was a UK chart topper for guitar band Coldplay.

50. MUSIC Of The Spheres was a UK hit album for which ex-member of The Stone Roses?

Answers on Page 166

PUMPING ON YOUR STEREO

ANSWERS:

1. Tom Jones; 2. Lloyd Cole & the Commotions;
3. Stranded; 4. Stereophonics; 5. The Manic Street
Preachers; 6. Madonna; 7. David Cassidy;
8. Usher; 9. The Album; 10. Lenny Kravitz;
11. Stevie Wonder; 12. U2; 13. Simple Minds;
14. Graceland; 15. Version 2.0; 16. Paul Weller;
17. In The City by The Jam; 18. Frankie Goes To
Hollywood; 19. Zenyatta Mondatta; 20. David
Gray; 21. The Pogues; 22. Jagged Little Pill;
23. The Fatboy Slim; 24. Dire Straits; 25. Bruce
Springsteen; 26. The Blue Nile; 27. Kylie;
28. Jamiroquai; 29. Pink Floyd; 30. Adam Ant;
31. The Beastie Boys; 32. Ian Dury & the
Blockheads; 33. Starsailor; 34. Enya; 35. Stories
From The City Stories From The Sea; 36. Shania
Twain; 37. Blink 182; 38. Eva Cassidy; 39. Elvis
Costello; 40. Get Yer Ya-yas Out; 41. Prince;
42. Cliff; 43. Pulp; 44. Radiohead; 45. The Who;
46. Travis; 47. George Harrison; 48. R.E.M.;
49. Parachutes; 50. Ian Brown.

DON'T STOP TILL YOU GET ENOUGH

MICHAEL Jackson exploded back on to the pop scene in 2001 with the single You Rock My World ... from his latest album Invincible. Is Jacko back to stay – or has his career peaked? You decide.

**Let's look back at the phenomenal career
of the self styled, King of Pop.**

1.   IN which US city was Michael raised?

2.   FOR which influential Detroit-based record
label did Michael and his brothers audition in
1968?

3.   WHAT was the title of The Jackson Five's
debut single in 1969?

4.   NAME Michael's first solo UK hit from 1972.

5.   HE starred with Diana Ross in a remake of a
classic Hollywood movie. What was his film
called?

6.   MICHAEL was chosen to narrate an album
based on a Steven Spielberg movie in 1982.
Name it.

7.   THE title track of his 1982 album Thriller
produced one of pop's all-time great videos.
Who was the singer's female co-star in the
classic promo?

8.   THAT same year, Michael had a hit duet with Paul
McCartney. What was the title of the song?

9.   WHICH rock star did he recruit to play the guitar
solo on Beat It in 1983?

10. ALSO IN 1983, Michael signed what was then the
largest individual sponsorship deal in pop history.
What product did he endorse?

Answers on Page 170

11. WHO was the fellow Motown legend that Michael co-wrote the USA for Africa charity single, We Are The World?

12. MICHAEL splashed out $47.5 million to buy what?

13. HE also starred as a space ship commander in a 3-D adventure at Disneyworld. What was he called?

14. WHAT is the name of Jacko's lavish California theme-park style home?

15. HIS best buddy was a baby chimp. What was its name?

16. JACKO married the daughter of another pop legend. Who was she?

17. WHAT was his first single to enter the UK charts at No.1?

18. WHO did Michael duet with on his 1987 No.1 single, I Just Can't Stop Loving You?

19. IN 1995, Jacko scored the UK Christmas No.1. With which single?

20. WHICH Hollywood screen legend got married for the seventh time in a ceremony on the singer's ranch?

Answers on Page 170

DON'T STOP TILL YOU GET ENOUGH

ANSWERS:

1. Gary, Indiana; 2. Motown; 3. I Want You Back;
4. Got To Be There; 5. The Wiz; 6. ET – The
Extra Terrestrial; 7. Ola Rey; 8. The Girl Is Mine;
9. Eddie Van Halen; 10. Pepsi Cola; 11. Lionel
Richie; 12. ATV Music ... which published 250
classic Beatles' songs; 13. Captain Eo;
14. Neverland; 15. Bubbles; 16. Lisa Marie Presley
– daughter of Elvis; 17. Black Or White in 1991;
18. Siedah Garrett; 19. Earth Song; 20. Elizabeth
Taylor.

SO YOU WIN AGAIN

WELL, how have you fared? Are you a real music mastermind ... or is it more like top of the flops?

One last burst of pot luck questions to really find out if you have what it takes to be a true pop genius.

1. JON Anderson is the singer with which legendary UK band?

2. WHICH superstar appeared as the Ace Face in The Who's movie, Quadrophenia?

3. WHAT was the character played by David Essex in the films, That'll Be The Day and Stardust?

4. OZZY Osbourne had a hit single with Down To Earth ... who is his manager?

5. THE Bonzo Dog Doo-Dah Band had their biggest hit with Urban Spaceman in 1968 ... Who produced it?

6. WHICH UK soul star invited TV chef Jamie Oliver round to his mansion earlier this year to cook dinner for his band?

7. WHICH group covered the classic Rod Stewart hit Hancbags And Gladrags in 2001?

8. WHO were Paul Rodgers, Andy Fraser, Paul Kossoff and Simon Kirke?

9. NAME the Sheffield group who had a smash hit in 1981 with the landmark electro-pop album, Dare.

10. WHO covered the Simon and Garfunkel classic America at the World Trade Centre benefit gig at Madison Square Garden, New York, in October 2001?

Answers on Page 174

SO YOU WIN AGAIN ...

1. Yes; 2. Sting; 3. Jim Maclaine; 4. His long suffering wife, Sharon; 5. Paul McCartney; 6. Jay Kay of Jamiroquai; 7. Stereophonics; 8. Legendary rock supergroup, Free; 9. The Human League; 10. David Bowie.

Also available:

You are my Larsson: The Henrik Larsson Story	£5.95
The Martin O'Neill Story	£5.95
The 2002 Prize Crossword Book	£4.99
The Billy Sloan Rock and Pop Quiz Book	£4.99
The Jim Traynor/Hugh Keevins Sports Quiz Book	£4.99
Joe Punter At The Races	£4.99
The Tam Cowan Joke Book	£4.99
VIDEO: Lubo – A Gift From God	£14.99

All these books are available at your local bookshop or newsagent, or can be ordered direct form the publisher. Indicate the number of copies required and fill in the form below.

Send to: *First Press Publishing,*
               Daily Record and Sunday Mail,
               1 Central Quay,
               Glasgow, G3 8DA

or phone: **0141 309 1425** quoting title, author and credit or debit card number.

or fax: **0141 309 3304**, quoting title, author and credit or debit card number.

or email: **orders@first-press.co.uk**

Enclose a remittance* to the value of the cover price plus 75p per book for postage and packing. European customers allow £1.50 per book for post and packing.

* Payment may be made in sterling by UK personal cheque, Eurocheque, postal order, sterling draft or international money order, made payable to First Press Publishing.

Alternatively by Visa/Mastercard/Debit Card Card No.

Expiry Date ☐☐☐☐   Valid From Date ☐☐☐☐   Issue Number ☐

Signature: _____

Applicable only in the UK and BFPO addresses.

While every effort is made to keep prices low, it is sometimes necessary to increase prices at short notice. First Press Publishing reserve the right to show on covers and charges new retail prices which may differ form those advertised in the text or elsewhere.

NAME AND ADDRESS (IN BLOCK CAPITALS PLEASE)

Name _____

Address _____

_____

_____Postcode_____

First Press will use your information for administration and analysis. We may share it with carefully selected third parties. We, or they, may send you details of goods and services. The information may be provided by letter, telephone or other. If you do not want your details to be shared please tick this box. ☐